British Museum

FUN BOOK

ANCIENT GREECE

Sandy Ra
Illustrated by David Farris

THE BRITISH MUSEUM PRESS

Text © Sandy Ransford 1999
Illustrations © David Farris 1999

Published by British Museum Press
A division of The British Museum Company Ltd
38 Russell Square, London WC1B 3QQ
britishmuseum.org/publishing

First published 1999
Reprinted 2006, 2012, 2013

A catalogue record for this book is available from the British Library

ISBN 978-0-7141-2168-0

Designed and illustrated by David Farris
Cover design by Joy FitzSimmons and David Farris
Printed by Oriental Press Dubai

CONTENTS

WHY DID ANCIENT GREEK OPTICIANS GO TO THE OLYMPIC GAMES?

BECAUSE IT WAS SUCH A SPECTACLE!

INTRODUCTION

Ancient Greece makes us think of great writers, thinkers and scientists; of gods and temples; of heroes who performed impossible feats; of terrifying monsters; of the first Olympic Games; and of wars and murders. Often it is very difficult to know which people and happenings were real and which were legendary, so if you find it all a bit confusing, don't worry, you are not alone! (If you don't know your Aristotle from your Eurydice, look them up in the checklist opposite to help you solve some of the puzzles.)

This book is a collection of puzzles based on the people, events and legends of ancient Greece. Crosswords, word-searches, bewildering brainteasers and tantalising picture puzzles will test and perplex you, but for a bit of light relief there are games to play and lots of ancient Greek jokes to keep you chuckling. Have fun!

WHO WROTE *TAKEAWAY MEALS IN ANCIENT GREECE?*

PLATO CHIPS.

Checklist

Achilles   Greek hero who fought in the Trojan War.

Agamemnon   King of Mycenae, a city in southern Greece, the remains of which can still be seen.

Amazons   a race of warrior women.

Aristotle   Greek philosopher who lived from 384 to 322 BC, a pupil of Plato.

Eurydice   Orpheus's wife, whom he tried to bring back from the world of the dead.

Herakles (Hercules)   Greek hero of enormous strength, who performed twelve famous tasks or labours.

Homer   The author of *The Iliad* and *The Odyssey*.

Jason   Greek hero who led the Argonauts on the quest for the Golden Fleece.

Odysseus   Greek hero who fought at Troy and then had a series of adventures on his way home which were recounted as *The Odyssey*.

Oedipus   the son of Laius and Jocasta, king and queen of Thebes, who went into exile to avoid fulfilling the prophecy that he would kill his father and marry his mother.

Orpheus   a legendary poet and musician.

Penelope   wife of Odysseus.

Plato   philosopher, who lived from 428 to 348 BC and wrote a famous book called *Republic*.

Socrates   philosopher, who lived from 470 to 399 BC and who taught Plato.

Spartan   someone who lived in Sparta. The Spartans were known for their toughness and ability to live on a poor diet under difficult conditions.

Sphinx   a monster who lived at Thebes and asked riddles, gobbling up anyone who got the answer wrong or who couldn't answer.

Troy   the city to which the Greeks laid siege when Paris, son of Priam, King of Troy, ran away with Helen, wife of Menelaus, King of Sparta.

Zeus   the king of the gods.

TESTING TIME

See how much you know about ancient Greece with this testing quiz. You have a one in three chance of getting each question right!

1 THE ACROPOLIS IS:
a) a temple in Athens
b) a theatre in Athens
c) a hill in Athens?

2 PEGASUS WAS A WINGED HORSE RIDDEN BY:
a) Icarus
b) Bellerophon
c) Daedalus?

3 WHO WROTE THE ILIAD? WAS IT:
a) Socrates
b) Homer
c) Euripides?

4 WHO WAS PLATO? WAS HE:
a) a philosopher
b) a king
c) a god?

5 WHOSE SON WAS PARIS? WAS HE THE SON OF:
a) Priam, King of Troy
b) Agamemnon, King of Mycenae
c) the god Zeus?

6 WHAT DID ACHILLES' MOTHER DO TO TRY TO PROTECT HER SON FROM INJURY, WHICH FAILED BECAUSE SHE OMITTED SOMETHING? DID SHE:
a) make a sacrifice to the gods
b) kill her other children
c) dip Achilles in the River Styx?

7 HERAKLES (OR HERCULES) WAS ORDERED BY APOLLO TO PERFORM TWELVE VERY DIFFICULT TASKS, OR LABOURS. THIS WAS A PUNISHMENT FOR:

a) killing his wife and children
b) insulting the gods
c) refusing to kill the Sphinx?

8 THE OLYMPIC GAMES WERE FIRST HELD:

a) before the 7th century BC
b) in the 5th century BC
c) in the 7th century AD?

9 ATHLETES WHO COMPETED IN THE OLYMPIC GAMES WORE:

a) tunics
b) fig leaves
c) nothing?

10 A CENTAUR WAS A MONSTER WHICH WAS:

a) part woman, part bird, part serpent
b) part man, part horse
c) part man, part horse, part bird?

11 THE PLACE WHERE THE DEAD RESIDED WAS CALLED:

a) Hades
b) Thessaly
c) Arcadia?

12 THE THREE-HEADED DOG THAT GUARDED THE HOME OF THE DEAD WAS CALLED:

a) Chimaera
b) Charybdis
c) Cerberus?

CROSSWORD CHALLENGE

See if you can solve all the clues in this tricky crossword. The numbers in brackets indicate how many letters the answer has.

Across

2 He is fabled for his stories (5)

4 One of the first gods, children of Uranus and Gaia. The word also means 'giant' (5)

6 A town in Greece which rivalled Athens (7)

8 The cloak of Zeus. To be under this means to be under protection (5)

9 A town in the west of Greece where Odysseus came from (6)

13 He governed Thebes after the death of Laius (5)

14 The name of Jason's ship (4)

16 A mountain thought to be the home of the gods (5, 7)

19 She changed Odysseus's companions into pigs (5)

20 In which to sail the seas (4)

21 The sea around Greece (6)

22 The king of Troy at the time of the Wooden Horse, and father of Hector (5)

Down

1 The Roman name for the god Dionysos (7)

3 A giant, and also the name of a group of stars (5)

5 The old king of Pylos at the time of the Trojan War (6)

7 A sea-god often shown blowing a conch shell (6)

8 One of a race of warrior women from Scythia (6)

10 Herakles's fifth task was to clean them (6, 7)

11 What Jason's companions were called (9)

12 Where the Olympic Games were held (7)

15 Jason and his companions sailed from Iolcos to here in search of the Golden Fleece (7)

17 A city in southern Greece, whose king at the time of the Trojan War was Agamemnon (7)

18 22 Across's daughter, who warned of the dangers of the Wooden Horse (9)

GOING TO THE THEATRE

The theatre at Epidaurus seated 12,300 people on 55 rows of benches. It still exists, and if you go to Greece you can visit it. Meanwhile, see how good your maths skills are with these testing questions about it.

1 If one row of benches seated 224 people, how many people would one eighth of the row seat?

2 If the chorus consisted of 20 dancers and 30 singers, what proportion of it are dancers?

3 If you add 12,300 to a particular whole number, the result will be greater than if you multiply that number by 12,300. What is the number?

DOES ZEUS LIVE IN OUR BATHROOM?

NO. WHAT MAKES YOU ASK THAT?

BECAUSE EVERY MORNING DAD BANGS ON THE DOOR AND SAYS 'OH, GOD, ARE YOU STILL IN THERE?'

MIRROR IMAGE

Narcissus was a handsome young man whom the gods caused to fall in love with his own reflection in a pool. If picture no. 1 shows the real Narcissus, which of the other pictures is the exact reflection of his image?

THE RIDDLE OF THE SPHINX

When Oedipus travelled away from Corinth to try to escape his destiny, he arrived in Thebes where he discovered that it was being terrorized by a monster called the Sphinx. With the head and chest of a woman, the body of a lion and the wings of a bird, the creature waylaid all travellers and asked them a riddle. Those who couldn't answer the riddle, or got it wrong, she ate. Oedipus decided to try his luck - and succeeded. Here is the riddle the Sphinx asked him. Can you solve it?

Which is the animal that has four feet in the morning, two at midday and three in the evening?

MORE RIDDLES

The answers to these may make you laugh!

1. What has three heads, two tails, eight legs, three bodies and two wings?
2. Where were the kings of ancient Greece crowned?
3. In which month did the ancient Greeks eat the least?
4. Why was a Greek amphitheatre a sad place?
5. Where did Homer go on his twentieth birthday?
6. What did Homer say to his wife when he arrived back at the house?
7. What was the highest mountain in Greece before Mount Olympus was discovered?
8. What was the difference between Helen of Troy and an ancient Greek mouse?
9. Where could Pan lay his pipes so no one could jump over them?
10. Why was Agamemnon buried at Mycenae?

KNOCK, KNOCK.

WHO'S THERE?

ACHILLES.

ACHILLES WHO?

ACHILLES MOSQUITOES IF THEY DON'T STOP BITING ME!

IT'S ALL GREEK TO ME!

Below is the ancient Greek alphabet.

A	a	N	n
B	b	Ξ	x
Γ	g	O	o
Δ	d	Π	p
E	e	P	r
Z	z	Σ	s
H	e	T	t
Θ	th	Y	u
I	i	Φ	ph
K	k	X	ch
Λ	l	Ψ	ps
M	m	Ω	o

Using it as a code, can you work out what the following words are?

1 ΖΕΥΣ

2 ΑΠΟΛΛΟ

3 ΜΑΡΑΘΟΝ

4 ΠΕΝΕΛΟΠΕ

5 ΑΘΕΝΣ

6 ΔΕΛΦΙ

ESCAPE FROM THE LABYRINTH

King Minos kept the Minotaur, a monster with the head of a bull and the body of a man, in a labyrinth (or maze) in Crete, and fed it each year on the flesh of seven youths and seven maidens from Athens. Theseus killed the Minotaur. With the help of King Minos's daughter, Ariadne, who gave him a ball of string, Theseus found his way out of the labyrinth. Can you do the same?

PILLARS OF WISDOM

The names of all the Greek gods and goddesses listed below can be traced out in this temple-shaped grid. The words may read across, up, down or diagonally, either forwards or backwards, but they are all in straight lines. Use a pencil and a ruler to help you find them.

APHRODITE

APOLLO

ARES

ARTEMIS

ATHENA

DEMETER

DIONYSOS

EROS

GAIA

GANYMEDE

HECATE

HEPHAISTOS

HERA

HERMES

HESTIA

KRONOS

PERSEPHONE

POSEIDON

RHEA

URANUS

ZEUS

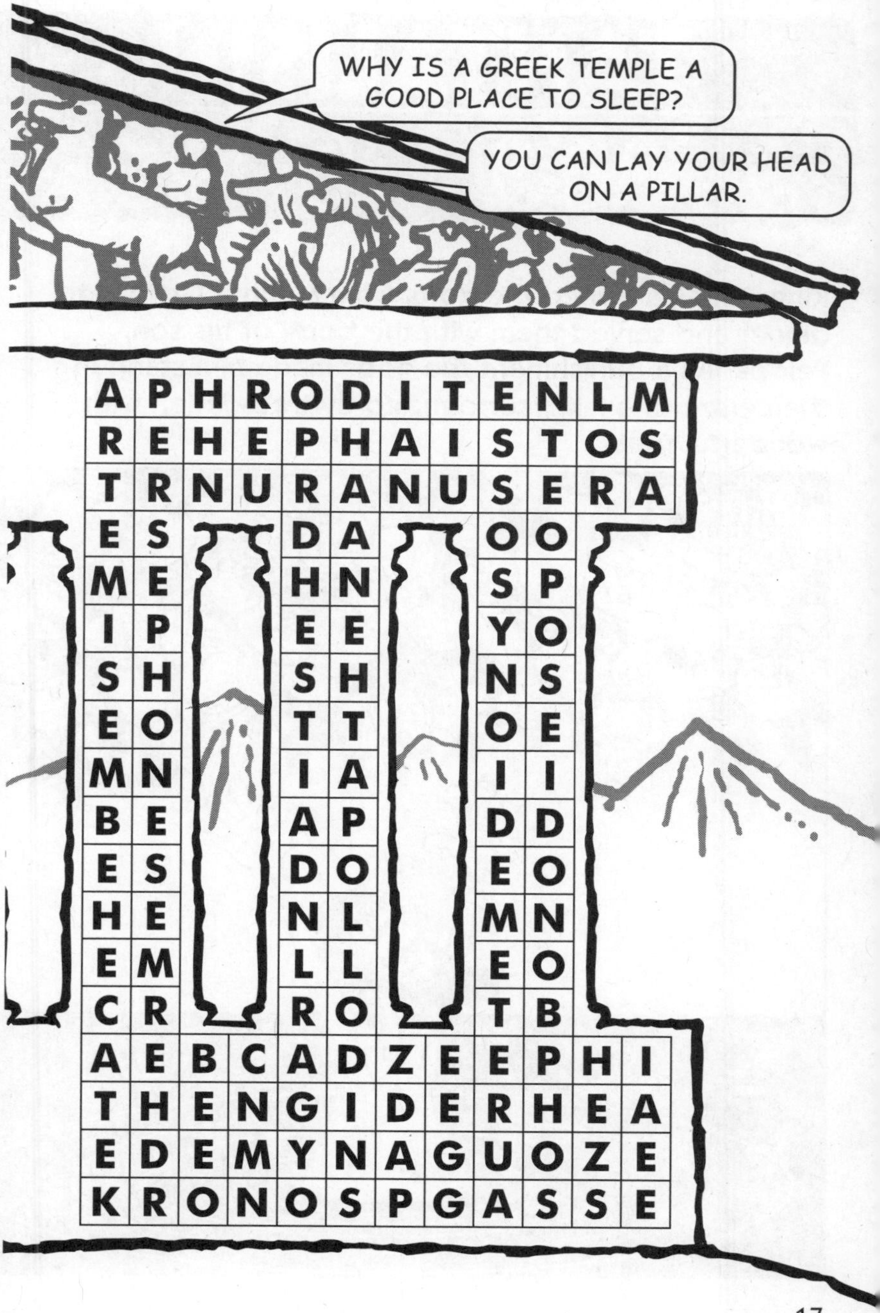

A	P	H	R	O	D	I	T	E	N	L	M
R	E	H	E	P	H	A	I	S	T	O	S
T	R	N	U	R	A	N	U	S	E	R	A
E	S			D	A			O	O		
M	E			H	N			S	P		
I	P			E	E			Y	O		
S	H			S	H			N	S		
E	O			T	T			O	E		
M	N			I	A			I	I		
B	E			A	P			D	D		
E	S			D	O			E	O		
H	E			N	L			M	N		
E	M			L	L			E	O		
C	R			R	O			T	B		
A	E	B	C	A	D	Z	E	E	P	H	I
T	H	E	N	G	I	D	E	R	H	E	A
E	D	E	M	Y	N	A	G	U	O	Z	E
K	R	O	N	O	S	P	G	A	S	S	E

TANTALISING

King Tantalus invited the gods from Mount Olympus to dinner and served them with the body of his son, Pelops. As a punishment the gods made him stand in the centre of a lake, surrounded by trees laden with wonderful fruits.

But the fruits were always just out of his reach, and when he tried to drink the water it receded. How many differences can you spot between these two pictures of him? Look closely, there may be more than you think.

BATHTIME

This kind of puzzle is called an acrostic. Solve the clues and fill in the answers in the grid opposite and you will find, reading down the arrowed column, the name of a Greek who had a very famous bath!

1 The only great Greek woman athlete (8)

2 He flew too close to the sun (6)

3 A famous mathematician whose name we associate with geometry (9)

4 A Greek philosopher whom we know for his theorem about triangles (10)

5 The 'ant people' who followed Achilles to the siege of Troy (9)

6 The science connected with clue 3 (8)

7 Achilles's weak point (4)

8 The goddess of love (9)

9 What a certain Greek philosopher cried when running naked from his bath (6)

10 The god of health and healing (9)

CONSULTING THE ORACLE

In ancient Greek times people used to ask questions of a priest or priestess. They believed the answers they got came from the gods themselves. But the answers were very often capable of being understood in more than one way, which made them very confusing. Here are some answers given by the oracle. Can you understand what they mean?

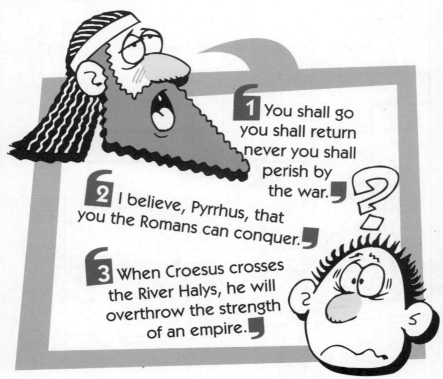

1 You shall go you shall return never you shall perish by the war.

2 I believe, Pyrrhus, that you the Romans can conquer.

3 When Croesus crosses the River Halys, he will overthrow the strength of an empire.

. . . something beginning with G. How many things beginning with G can you spot in the picture?

23

HEROES ALL

There aren't any clues in this crossword - all you have to do is fit the names of all the Greek heroes into the right places in the grid. Each word will only fit in one place! The words are listed according to the numbers of their letters, and the way to start is by filling in the words in the smallest groups. To help avoid any confusion, we've given you three letters in the grid.

4 LETTERS
AJAX
AIAS

5 LETTERS
JASON

6 LETTERS
AENEAS
CADMUS
CASTOR
HECTOR
PELOPS
PELEUS
POLLUX

7 LETTERS
CECROPS
ORPHEUS
PERSEUS
THESEUS

8 LETTERS
ACHILLES
HERAKLES
MELEAGER
MENELAUS
ODYSSEUS
SISYPHUS

9 LETTERS
AGAMEMNON

11 LETTERS
BELLEROPHON

12 LETTERS
ERICHTHONIUS

SYMBOLIC

These mathematical puzzles are based roughly on Mycenaean Linear B writing. Each symbol stands for a number (though each puzzle has its own set of symbols, just to make it harder!). Can you make sense of the sums?

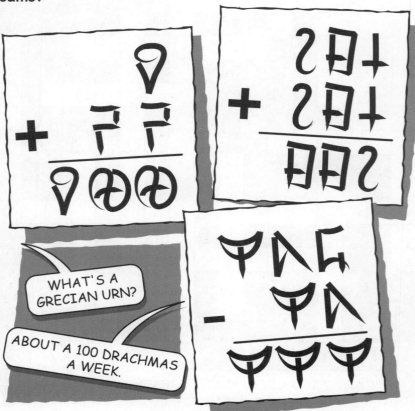

WHAT'S A GRECIAN URN?

ABOUT A 100 DRACHMAS A WEEK.

MUSIC MAN

Orpheus was famous for his skill in playing the lyre.
Out of these six pictures of him playing, which two are
exactly the same?

GET A HEAD!

All the monsters listed below can be traced out in this grid shaped like Medusa's head. They may read across, up, down or diagonally, either forwards or backwards, but they are all in straight lines. Use a pencil and a ruler to help you find them.

CENTAUR

MEDUSA

CERBERUS

MINOTAUR

CHARYBDIS

CHIMAERA

NEMEAN LION
(2 LINES)

CHIRON

POLYPHEMUS

CRETAN BULL
(2 LINES)

GERYON SCYLLA

GORGON

SPHINX

HYDRA SIRENS

STHENO

STYMPHALIAN BIRDS
(2 LINES)

LAESTRYGONIANS TYPHON

MARES OF DIOMEDES
(3 LINES)

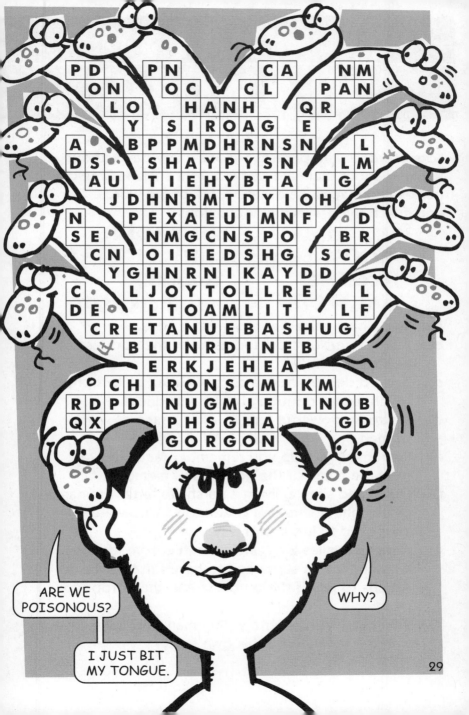

29

WHAT'S IN A WORD?

Lots of words and phrases we use every day without thinking about them are derived from ancient Greek names and places. Below are some of the words. Can you match them with their definitions?

1 AMAZON
2 CYNIC
3 HYGIENE
4 MARATHON
5 MNEMONIC
6 PYRRHIC VICTORY
7 SPARTAN
8 NARCISSISTIC

a) Something gained at too great a price.
b) A word derived from the name of the goddess of health.
c) A word derived from a sect of Greek philosophers which means doubting human goodness.
d) A strong, powerful female, after a race of warrior women.
e) Something to help you remember facts, derived from the name of the goddess of memory.
f) Frugal and simple, living a harsh life, after the name of the inhabitants of a Greek town who were supposed to live in this way.
g) A race 26 miles long, after a battle from which a messenger was supposed to have run 23 miles to Athens to tell of the outcome and then dropped dead.
h) Being very vain, after a young man who fell in love with the reflection of his own face.

Look at these four pictures of a Grecian urn. One thing (a different thing each time) is missing from each picture. Can you spot what the missing things are?

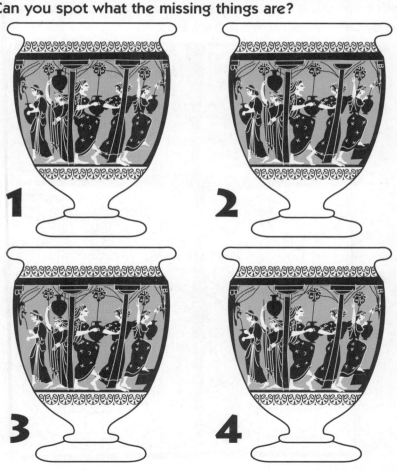

1

2

3

4

RUB A DUB DUB...

. . . it's a man in a tub. He was a philosopher called Diogenes. In these drawings of him one thing (a different thing each time) has been added to pictures 2 to 6. Can you spot what they are?

THE ODYSSEY GAME

In *The Odyssey* Homer recorded the adventures of
Odysseus on his voyage home from Troy. It took many
years, and he had to combat many perils. He was away
for so long that people urged his wife, Penelope, to re-
marry, and eventually she agreed to do so, but not until
she had finished weaving a shroud for Odysseus's father,
who was an old man and not expected to live for much
longer. This was a clever move, for Penelope wove the
shroud each day and then secretly unpicked her work
each night, so the shroud never progressed much
further. Eventually, however, one of her maids betrayed
her, and her furious suitors besieged her palace and
plotted the murder of her son, Telemachus. This was the
situation Odysseus eventually returned to after he had
defeated the Cyclops, evaded the Sirens and Scylla and
Charybdis, and escaped from Calypso's island.

You can have fun playing a game based on
Odysseus's travels if you turn to the next two pages.
Two or more players can take part, or you could even
play on your own. Each player needs a counter, and
you'll need a die and something to shake it in. Play it like
any other board game: players take turns to shake the
die and move the number of squares the die shows. If
you land on one of the marked squares you have to
follow the instructions on it. The first player to finish wins
the game.

ON ISLAND OF OGYGIA WITH CALYPSO - MISS A TURN

THROW A 6 TO ESCAPE FROM CHARYBDIS

RECOGNISED BY DOG ARGUS - MOVE FORWARD 2 PLACES

MEET THE SCYLLA - GO BACK 4 PLACES

PASS THE ARROW TEST - FORWARD TO HOME

CHALLENGED BY PENELOPE'S SUITORS - GO BACK 4 PLACES

MEET THE SIRENS - GO BACK 5 PLACES

HOME

SOLDIERING ON

How many soldiers can you find hidden in our version of the wooden horse? That is, how many times can you find the word SOLDIER in the grid? The words may read across, up, down or diagonally, either forwards or backwards, but they are all in straight lines.

GONE MISSING

In each of these groups of words every other letter is missing. Can you fill them in and work out what the words are? The clues in brackets should help.

1 A-H-N- T-R-N-
T-O- M-C-N-E (TOWNS)

2 C-E-E R-O-E-
C-P-U- S-C-L- (ISLANDS)

3 A-G-A- A-R-A-I-
L-B-A-
M-D-T-R-A-E-N (SEAS)

4 A-H-N- A-T-M-S
H-S-I- D-M-T-R (GODDESSES)

5 M-D-S M-N-L-U-
P-I-M N-S-O- (KINGS)

EYE, EYE!

Argus was supposed to have **100 eyes**, which, after Mercury had killed him, were set on the peacock's tail.

Is this drawing of him correct? How many eyes does this creature have?

Hope I never need glasses...

CROSSWORD CHALLENGE

Across

1 **Eros's wife** *(6)*

3 **The earth goddess and 'universal mother'** *(4)*

6 **The second wife of Priam of Troy, who was turned into a dog and threw herself in the sea** *(6)*

8 **The nymph with whom Odysseus spent eight years on the island of Ogygia, and the name of a kind of West Indian song** *(7)*

10 **Odysseus's wife** *(8)*

11 **The nine-headed serpent which Herakles killed** *(5)*

12 **The Olympic Games had races for two- and four-horse ones** *(7)*

14 **See 16 Down**

15 **The centre for the worship of Apollo, and where the Pythian Games were held** *(6)*

18 **The priest of Apollo who was crushed to death by a serpent** *(7)*

20 **She helped, and later married, Jason, but committed a number of horrible murders** *(5)*

21 **A tree-nymph, such as Eurydice** *(5)*

23 **He was remembered for killing his father and marrying his mother** *(7)*

24 **The patron goddess of Athens** *(6)*

Down

2 **A giant with only one eye** *(7)*

4 **The sun god son of Zeus** *(6)*

5 **The god of forests, flocks and herds** *(3)*

7 **The cup-bearer of Zeus** *(8)*

9 **The Trojan hero who was killed by Achilles and dragged around the town's walls** *(6)*

13 **The wife of Menelaus whose elopement with Paris brought about the Trojan War** *(5)*

15 **The god of wine** *(8)*

16 and 14 Across **What Jason and the Argonauts set out to find** *(6, 6)*

17 **The gods' messenger** *(6)*

18 **Victors in the Pythian Games wore wreaths made from this bush** *(6)*

19 **Oedipus's mother** *(7)*

22 **One of Herakles's tasks was to bring back these fruits of the Hesperides** *(6)*

LADIES' GAME

Because the Olympic Games were closely connected with preparing soldiers for war, women did not take part in them. They did, however, play ball games and knucklebones, which was rather like jacks or five stones. Any number of players can take part. Each needs five small stones and a bouncy ball.

Number the pebbles on both sides with a felt-tipped pen, so whichever way up they fall you can see their number. To play, scatter the pebbles on the ground, then throw the ball up in the air. With the hand that threw the ball you must pick up pebble no. 1 before the ball bounces, transfer the pebble to the other hand and then catch the ball before it bounces a second time. You then throw the ball up again and pick up pebble no. 2 in the same way, and continue to play until you have picked up all five pebbles in the correct order. If you drop a pebble, pick one up in the wrong order, let the ball bounce a second time, or fail to catch it, then you are out of the game. The winner is the first person to complete the game without making a mistake.

WHERE WOULD I FIND A GREEK TEMPLE?

ON THE SIDE OF A GREEK'S FOREHEAD.

OLYMPIC GAMES

We do not know when the first Olympic Games were held, but the Greeks started numbering them in 776 BC. They held a great five-day festival at Olympia, in western Greece, every four years in August. This was after the harvest had been gathered in and people were free to attend the Games. The contests included: two- and four-horse chariot races; a pentathlon comprising discus- and javelin-throwing, the long jump, running and wrestling; the *pankration* - a combination of no-holds-barred boxing and wrestling; and the *hoplitodromos*, a running race in armour, for the physical fitness required by the Games was intended to prepare men for fighting as soldiers. There were three running races: the sprint, and two long-distance races called the *dolikhos* and the *diaulos*. Can you rearrange the odd-looking words below to make events held at the Games?

1 SUSCID 2 NAJVEIL 3 PIGNUMJ
5 GRINNUN 6 TRIGNEWLS
4 SOLIDAU
7 NIXGOB 8 SHODKOIL
9 INKTARPONA 10 MOODSHOPTROIL

43

BUILDING SITE

44

The pictures on this page and the opposite page tell a story, but they are in the wrong order. Can you rearrange them into the correct order?

A number of famous names and things are written below
- but they're in the form of pictures plus or minus letters.
For example, this picture:

- T + SP = SPARTAN

Can you work out what all the others are?

1 - K + - C =

2 + =

3 - E + - IL =

4 - T + S + - R - S + C + L =

5 - Y + E - C + D =

6 + X + & + =

What connects
numbers 1 and 2?

46

When Icarus flew with his father Daedalus from Crete he went too close to the sun. The wax which held on his wings melted and he fell into the sea. Look closely at this picture of Icarus. How many of the feathers on his wings are scorched by the sun, and how many are not?

ALPHABETICAL

Here's a puzzle to test your wits! It's very easy if you do it slowly - but not if you don't!

1	Write down all the letters of the alphabet.
2	Cross out letter 2 and the letter that comes two spaces after it.
3	Remove letters 6 and 7.
4	Take away the letter whose number is five times the value of the first letter you removed, and the four letters that follow it.
5	Reverse the order of the next two letters, and put letter 16 before them.
6	Put letters 8 and 9 at the front of the word.
7	Take away letter 17, bring in the second letter you left at the beginning and add letter 18.
8	Add the first letter you left at the beginning.
9	Add letter 20 and the second vowel.
10	Take away the last six letters.
11	Add the letter that follows letter 18.

What have you got? And do you know who or what it is?

ARE YOU STAYING LONG IN ATHENS?

NO, WE'RE PARTHENON.

DEEP FRIEZE

How many differences can you spot between these two
pictures of the Parthenon frieze?

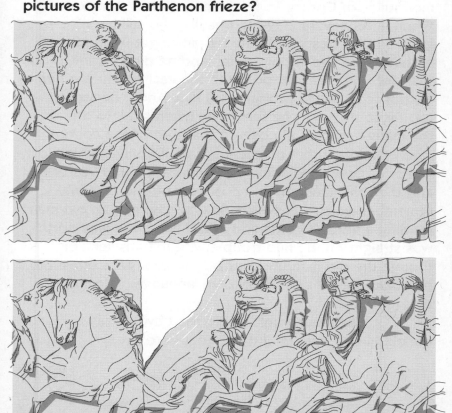

LOST IN TIME

A traveller was wandering northwards through the mountains of Greece in search of a fabled monster. When, after several days' journeying, he still hadn't arrived at his destination, he began to get worried that he had taken the wrong route. And he didn't want to do that, for if he strayed too far to the east he knew a fierce warrior tribe would probably kill him. And if he strayed too far to the west, he feared he might fall into one of the many ravines that covered that part of the country. And he had another problem. He could only speak two words of Greek. He knew that *ne* meant either yes or no, and that *ohi* meant either no or yes, but he couldn't remember which was which. So when he met an old man tending a herd of goats and asked him if the way north was straight on, he had trouble with the answer. For though the old man understood the stranger's question, he could only answer in his own language. '*Ne*,' replied the goat herd.

What four words could the traveller say to enable him to understand the goat herd's reply?

WHAT DID ONE ARCHAEOLOGIST SAY TO THE OTHER?

'LET'S GO AND HAVE A CUP OF TEA AND TALK ABOUT OLD TIMES.'

MOUNTAINEERING

Can you find the path that leads to the top of Mount Olympus?

I THINK, THEREFORE I AM

The names of all the famous Greek philosophers listed below can be traced out in the grid opposite. But unlike the other word searches, this puzzle's words read in a continuous line which snakes round the grid, going forwards, backwards, up or down, but *not* diagonally. All the letters in the grid are used, but each is used once only. We have shown you where to start.

ANAXIMANDER   HERACLITUS

ANAXIMENES   PARMENIDES

ANAXAGORUS   PLATO

ANTISTHENES   PLOTINUS

ARISTOTLE   PROTAGORAS

CHRYSIPPUS   PYTHAGORAS

DEMOCRITUS   SOCRATES

DIOGENES   THALES

EMPEDOCLES   XENOPHON

EPICURUS   ZENO

CROSSWORD CHALLENGE

The clues here are a mixture of word and pictures, easy and more difficult. The numbers in brackets show the number of letters in each answer.

Across

3 A word describing poetry meant to be sung; its first letters are the same as the beginning of an ancient Greek stringed instrument (5)

7 The god of fire, volcanoes, and blacksmithing (10)

8 Priestess of Venus who fell in love with Leander, also a man admired for his achievements (4)

10 The killing of an animal to please the gods (9)

12  (3)

15  (5)

16  (6)

18 The opposite of 'centre' (4)

19 (6)

20 The nine daughters of Zeus and Mnemosyne, goddesses of memory, arts and sciences (5)

Down

1 Where Oedipus's Sphinx lived (6)

2 You are in one at school! (5)

4 To put back (7)

5 Describing ancient Latin and Greek authors, it has the same beginning as clue 2 Down (7)

6 Ancient Greek armour was made of this metal mixture of copper and tin (6)

7  (6)

9  (7)

11 Bravery (7)

13 Armour covering the chest (7)

14 The opposite of 'attack' (6)

15 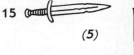 (5)

17 (4)

1. A famous ancient Greek had a warrior brother who was killed in a battle. The man who died didn't have a brother. So how were the famous ancient Greek and the dead warrior related?

2. Eight and twenty rabbits
Were grazing on a hill.
The Spartans killed a seventh part -
How many graze there still?

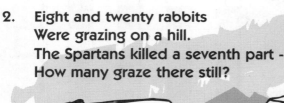

THE WOODEN RABBIT OF SPARTA

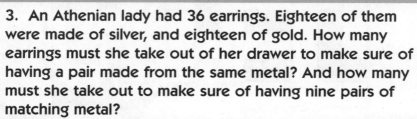

3. An Athenian lady had 36 earrings. Eighteen of them were made of silver, and eighteen of gold. How many earrings must she take out of her drawer to make sure of having a pair made from the same metal? And how many must she take out to make sure of having nine pairs of matching metal?

4. An Athenian farmer was driving his sheep to market. There were six sheep in front of a sheep, six sheep behind a sheep, and a sheep in the middle. How many sheep was he driving?

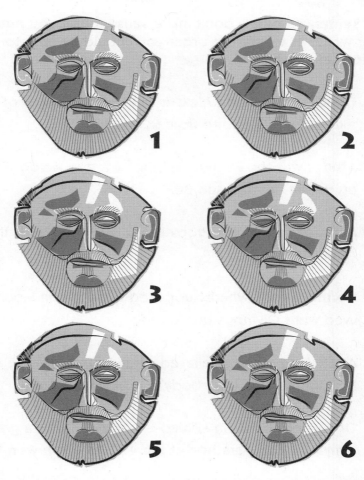

1

2

3

4

5

6

Which of these pictures of Agamemnon's death mask is the odd one out?

ALL MUDDLED UP

The sentences below don't make sense, but if you put their words in a different order you should be able to understand them.

1 The Great Macedon Alexander III lived 356 was of Alexander 323 to and from BC.

2 Athens was the Parthenon built between Acropolis on the 447 at 438 and BC.

3 Acropolis called the Propylaea of the gateway is the Athenian.

4 Northern gods where supposed Greece is in Mount lived were Olympus the to have.

5 A different person believed when born that Pythagoras died their body was again in a spirit.

6 Of Persians battle in Militiades victory and his a great army over the Marathon at the 490 Athenian won BC.

ANSWERS

Page 6 Testing Time

1. c) A hill in Athens.
2. b) Bellerophon.
3. b) Homer.
4. a) A philosopher.
5. a) Priam, King of Troy.
6. c) Dip Achilles in the River Styx.
7. a) Killing his wife and children.
8. a) Before the 7th century BC.
9. c) Nothing.
10. b) Part man, part horse.
11. a) Hades.
12. c) Cerberus.

Page 8 Crossword Challenge

Page 10 Going to the Theatre

1. 28 people.   2. Two-fifths. 3. 1.

Page 11 Mirror Image

Picture no. 4.

Page 12 The Riddle of the Sphinx

The human being, who crawls on all fours as a baby (morning), walks on two legs as an adult (midday) and walks with a stick (three legs) when elderly (evening).

Page 13 More Riddles

1. A person riding a horse carrying a chicken.
2. On the head.
3. The month with the shortest number of days.
4. Because its seats were in tiers.
5. Into his 21st year.
6. 'Honey, I'm Homer.'
7. Mount Olympus.
8. Helen charmed the he's; the mouse harmed the cheese.
9. In a corner of the room.
10. Because he was dead.

Page 14 It's All Greek to Me!

1. Zeus.   2. Apollo.
3. Marathon.   4. Penelope.
5. Athens.   6. Delphi.

Page 15 Escape from the Labyrinth

Page 16 Pillars of Wisdom

A	P	H	R	O	D	I	T	E	N	L	M
R	E	H	E	P	H	A	I	S	T	O	S
T	R	N	U	R	A	N	U	S	E	R	A
E	S		D	A			O	O			
M	E		H	N			S	P			
I	P		E	E			Y	O			
S	H		S	H			N	S			
E	O		T	T			O	E			
M	N		I	A			I	I			
B	E		A	P			D	D			
E	S		D	O			E	O			
H	E		N	L			M	N			
E	M		L	L			E	O			
C	R		R	O			T	B			
A	E	B	C	A	D	Z	E	E	P	H	I
T	H	E	N	G	I	D	E	R	H	E	A
E	D	E	M	Y	N	A	G	U	O	Z	E
K	R	O	N	O	S	P	G	A	S	S	E

Page 18 Tantalising

There are 20 differences.

Page 20 Bathtime

The arrowed column reads 'Archimedes', the philosopher. Archimedes discovered in his bath that the apparent loss in weight of a body immersed in water is equal to the weight of water displaced. He leapt out, exclaiming, 'Eureka!' (I have found it!).

Page 22 Consulting the Oracle

1. The meaning of this pronouncement depends on its punctuation. It may mean, 'You shall go, you shall return never, you shall perish by the war.' or 'You shall go, you shall return, never you shall perish by the war.'

2. 'You, Pyrrhus, can conquer the Romans.' or 'The Romans can conquer you, Pyrrhus.'

3. This pronouncement concerned a war Croesus was about to wage. He assumed it meant that he would overthrow the enemy's empire, but in fact he destroyed his own when he was defeated in the war.

Page 23

I Spy With My Little Eye . . .

The following things beginning with G can be spotted in the picture: gorgon; Ganymede; Golden Fleece; goat; giant; gate; garden; garland; glove; garments; goose; grapes; grave; gymnast; gutter; gable.

Page 24 Heroes All

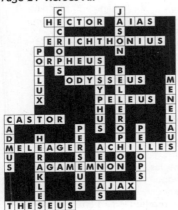

Page 26 Symbolic

1.
$$\begin{array}{r} 1 \\ +99 \\ \hline 100 \end{array}$$

2.
$$\begin{array}{r} 497 \\ +497 \\ \hline 994 \end{array}$$

3.
$$\begin{array}{r} 123 \\ -\ 12 \\ \hline 111 \end{array}$$

Page 27 Music Man
Pictures no. 4 and 5 are exactly the same.

Page 28 Get A Head!

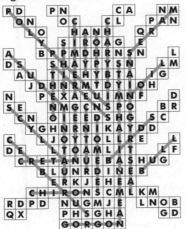

Page 30 What's In a Word?
1. Amazon - a strong, powerful female, after a race of warrior women.

2. Cynic - a word derived from a sect of Greek philosophers which means doubting human goodness.

3. Hygiene - a word derived from the goddess of health.

4. Marathon - a race 26 miles long, after a battle from which a messenger was supposed to have run 23 miles to Athens to tell of the outcome and then dropped dead.

5. Mnemonic - something to help you remember facts, derived from the name of the goddess of memory.

6. Pyrrhic victory - something gained at too great a price.

7. Spartan - frugal and simple, living a harsh life, after the name of the inhabitants of a Greek town who were supposed to live in this way.

8. Narcissistic - being very vain, after a young man who fell in love with the reflection of his own face.

Page 31 A Grecian Urn
Missing from the pictures are:

Page 32 Rub a Dub Dub . . .
Added to the pictures are:
2. shower cap   5. bath plug
3. mousehole   6. soap.
4. loofah

Page 36
Soldiering On
There are 18 SOLDIERs hidden in the horse.

Page 38 Gone Missing
1. ATHENS, TIRYNS, TROY, MYCENAE.
2. CRETE, RHODES, CYPRUS, SICILY.
3. AEGEAN, ADRIATIC, LIBYAN, MEDITERRANEAN.
4. ATHENA, ARTEMIS, HESTIA, DEMETER.
5. MIDAS, MENELAUS, PRIAM, NESTOR.

Page 39 Eye, Eye!
Our Argus has 101 eyes.

Page 40 Crossword Challenge

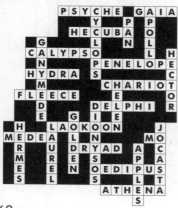

Page 43 Olympic Games
1. Discus.   2. Javelin.   3. Jumping.
4. Diaulos.   5. Running.   6. Wrestling.
7. Boxing.   8. Dolikhos.
9. Pankration.   10. Hoplitodromos.

Page 44 Building Site
The correct order of the pictures is:
5, 3, 8, 6, 1, 4, 7, 2.

Page 46 Step by Step
1. Socrates.
2. Hemlock.
3. Plato.
4. Sophocles.
5. Poseidon.
6. Alexander.
Socrates reputedly died after drinking hemlock.

Page 47 High Flyer
Icarus has 60 scorched feathers and 240 unscorched feathers.

Page 48 Alphabetical
You end up with Hippocrates, the ancient Greek physician who was called 'the father of modern medicine'.

Page 49 Deep Frieze
There are 10 differences between the two pictures.

Page 50 Lost in Time
'Did you say *ne*?' If the goat herd answers, '*Ne*,' then '*ne*' means yes. And if he answers, '*Ohi*,' then '*ohi*' means 'yes'. (In fact, '*ne*' does mean 'yes' in Greek.)

Page 51 Mountaineering

Page 52 I Think, Therefore I Am

Page 54 Crossword Challenge

Page 56 Mindbenders

1. The ancient Greek was the hero's sister.

2. None. The Spartans killed four; the rest would have fled.

3. a) Three. b) 19.

4. Seven.

Page 57 Odd One Out

Picture number 4 is the odd one out.

Page 58 All Muddled Up

1. Alexander the Great was Alexander III of Macedon and lived from 356 to 323 BC.

2. The Parthenon was built on the Acropolis at Athens between 447 and 438 BC.

3. The gateway of the Athenian Acropolis is called the Propylaea.

4. Mount Olympus, where the gods were supposed to have lived, is in northern Greece.

5. Pythagoras believed that when a person died their spirit was born again in a different body.

6. Miltiades and his Athenian army won a great victory over the Persians at the battle of Marathon in 490 BC.